Specific Skill Series

Drawing Conclusions

Richard A. Boning

Fifth Edition

SRA/McGraw-Hill

Columbus, Ohio

Cover, Back Cover, James D. Watt/Masterfile

SRA/McGraw-Hill

A Division of The **McGraw·Hill** *Companies*

Printed in the United States of America.

Send all inquiries to:
    SRA/McGraw-Hill
    8787 Orion Place
    Columbus, OH 43240-4027

ISBN 0-02-687986-7

7 8 IPC 02 01

To the Teacher

PURPOSE:

DRAWING CONCLUSIONS helps develop one of the most important interpretive skills. Pupils learn to look beyond the writer's literal statements to reach an unstated but logical conclusion based on those statements and sometimes their phrasing. In DRAWING CONCLUSIONS the correct conclusion is the most logical one for pupils to reach from only the information presented.

FOR WHOM:

The skill of DRAWING CONCLUSIONS is developed through a series of books spanning ten levels (Picture, Preparatory, A, B, C, D, E, F, G, H). The Picture Level is for pupils who have not acquired a basic sight vocabulary. The Preparatory Level is for pupils who have a basic sight vocabulary but are not yet ready for the first-grade-level book. Books A through H are appropriate for pupils who can read on levels one through eight, respectively. **The use of the *Specific Skill Series Placement Test* is recommended to determine the appropriate level.**

THE NEW EDITION:

The fifth edition of the *Specific Skill Series* maintains the quality and focus that has distinguished this program for more than 25 years. A key element central to the program's success has been the unique nature of the reading selections. Nonfiction pieces about current topics have been designed to stimulate the interest of students, motivating them to use the comprehension strategies they have learned to further their reading. To keep this important aspect of the program intact, a percentage of the reading selections have been replaced in order to ensure the continued relevance of the subject material.

In addition, a significant percentage of the artwork in the program has been replaced to give the books a contemporary look. The cover photographs are designed to appeal to readers of all ages.

SESSIONS:

Short practice sessions are the most effective. It is desirable to have a practice session every day or every other day, using a few units each session.

SCORING:

Pupils should record their answers on the reproducible worksheets. The worksheets make scoring easier and provide uniform records of the pupils' work. Using worksheets also avoids consuming the exercise books.

To the Teacher

It is important for pupils to know how well they are doing. For this reason, units should be scored as soon as they have been completed. Then a discussion can be held in which pupils justify their choices. (The Integrated Language Activities, many of which are open-ended, do not lend themselves to an objective score; thus there are no answer keys for these pages.)

GENERAL INFORMATION ON *DRAWING CONCLUSIONS*:

The questions in DRAWING CONCLUSIONS do not deal with direct references; thus the answers do not use the same words as the paragraphs. On the Picture Level, the readers examine the picture for the correct answer. The Preparatory, A, and B levels contain primarily indirect references; that is, the answers are found in the paragraphs but with slightly different wording. Some easy conclusions are also included. As the books advance in challenge, there are more difficult conclusions, involving less obvious relationships. The conclusions also become more dependent on qualifying words such as "mostly," "all," "some," or "only."

In DRAWING CONCLUSIONS the readers are asked to find an example, note a contrast, generalize, see cause and effect relationships, detect a mood, see an analogy, identify a time or place relationship, make a comparison, or anticipate an outcome.

It is important that the teacher ask pupils to find in the paragraph the specific information relevant to the tentative conclusion. Then pupils must test the conclusion against the information provided. When the emphasis is placed on finding evidence to prove answers and when the pupils put themselves in roles of detectives, not only does their ability to draw conclusions rapidly improve, but they also have fun.

Pupils must know that a conclusion is a judgment made. It must be supported by strong evidence. In DRAWING CONCLUSIONS the correct answer is one that is either highly likely or certain.

Some alternate answer choices may be true. The answer that is accepted as correct, however, must not only be true but must have supportive evidence in the paragraph. The clue may hinge on a single word, involve a phrase or a sentence, or encompass the paragraph as a whole.

RELATED MATERIALS:

Specific Skill Series Placement Tests, which enable the teacher to place pupils at their appropriate levels in each skill, are available for the Elementary (Pre-1–6) and Midway (4–8) grade levels.

About This Book

When you read, you can often figure out things that the writer doesn't tell you directly. You do this by thinking about the information the author does tell you. When you figure out something the author does not state directly, you are **drawing conclusions**.

Good readers draw conclusions as they read. They use the information the writer gives them to figure out things that the writer does not say. Read this paragraph. What conclusion can you draw about when Hawaii became a state?

> Hawaii and Alaska, which became states in the same year, are very different from each other. Alaska became the largest state when it joined the Union on January 3, 1959. Hawaii, the last state to join the Union, is one of the nation's smallest states.

Did you figure out that Hawaii became a state after January 3, 1959, but before January 1, 1960? You can draw this conclusion from the information the writer gives.

In this book, you will read paragraphs. After you read each paragraph, draw a conclusion about something in the paragraph. Use the information in the paragraph to figure out the correct answer.

1. In Fredericksburg, Virginia, the townspeople celebrate an annual October holiday that dates back to colonial days. The Fredericksburg Dog Mart is a one-day carnival at which all sorts of dogs are sold or exchanged. This trading day was proposed by the Native Americans as a truce with colonists in the late 1600s. Weapons would not be carried. The colonists' hunting dogs would be exchanged for furs, gold, and crafts.

2. Air Force personnel assigned to the jungle, tropics, or arctic always welcome suggestions from Sharee Pepper. A research biologist for the Air Force, Sharee herself has floated down jungle rivers, handled and eaten poisonous snakes, and swum alongside of sharks and barracudas. Her personal experiences have helped Sharee become an expert on survival in any environment.

3. Police are able to identify the gun that fired a particular bullet. If the police believe they have found the gun from which the bullet was fired, they fire another bullet from the same gun and compare the markings on the two bullets. The barrel of a gun leaves telltale marks on a bullet. The police see if the marks on both bullets are identical.

4. Would you like to go to school partially underground? This is what children in some towns are doing. Because fuel for heat costs so much, people want a school building that doesn't have to be heated as much. They build the school underground because the earth around it stays warm in winter. Big glass windows on the roof catch and keep the sun's heat.

5. The police sometimes use an electronic microscope instead of an ordinary one. This instrument can enlarge a tiny dust particle to 100,000 times its actual size. If this microscope were big enough to enlarge a person of average size, the person would seem to be about four hundred times as tall as the Empire State Building!

1. You can tell that—

   (A) Native Americans still trade in Fredericksburg
   (B) the colonists hunted with the Native Americans
   (C) the Native Americans and colonists had quarrels
   (D) the Native Americans made weapons for the colonists

2. You can tell that Sharee—

   (A) died from snake poison
   (B) likes adventure
   (C) likes to fly
   (D) makes a lot of money

3. The markings on bullets fired from the same gun—

   (A) can't be identified
   (B) are like fingerprints
   (C) are in no way similar to footprints
   (D) never match

4. You can tell that the school—

   (A) closes down on cloudy days
   (B) has happy students
   (C) can't be seen from the ground
   (D) has no windows in its walls

5. The difference between an ordinary microscope and an electronic one is—

   (A) size
   (B) color
   (C) weight
   (D) magnifying power

1.   Why do presidents and royalty receive a twenty-one-gun salute when they visit another nation? It is a show of friendship, not of war. In olden times, when a foreign ruler sailed into a port for a visit, both nations wanted to show that their guns were empty—they were planning no surprise attack. So they fired their cannons into the air. Twenty-one was chosen as being three times the lucky number seven.

2.   Before settlers from the East came to the western plains, the prairie dogs had their own "towns." Some prairie dog towns covered six thousand square miles and housed a million of these little rodents. The entrances to the prairie dogs' underground homes are mounds of mud, often a foot high, separated by twenty or thirty feet. Today, prairie dog towns are fewer and smaller.

3.   Oysters are often planted in and harvested from bays. Oyster farmers use surface buoys to mark the locations of their oyster "crops." Before the young oysters are planted, the farmer makes an area of bay bottom firm with shells and tiles. Attacked by fish and other sea creatures, oysters have one chance in a million to reach adult size. Those that survive are brought up from the bottom of the bay and sold.

4.   Some scientists now believe that humans have a tendency to adopt a forty-eight-hour day rather than a twenty-four-hour day, if they have no way of gauging time. French scientists have conducted an experiment with two volunteers without clocks in a deep cave. After a period of time, the volunteers fell into forty-eight-hour cycles—thirty-six hours of work followed by twelve hours of sleep.

5.   To help sell more wool, a sixteenth-century English ruler made it a law that everyone seven years of age and older must wear a cap of wool. Anyone who did not was fined. So important was the wool business to England that, as late as 1826, it was a crime punishable by death to take sheep out of the country to be sold.

UNIT 2

1. You can tell that in olden times—
   (A) no one believed in lucky numbers
   (B) everyone carried a gun
   (C) many presidents were shot
   (D) rulers sometimes used surprise attacks

2. From the story we can't tell—
   (A) the size of the towns
   (B) whether the number of towns has increased or decreased
   (C) what the "doorways" were like
   (D) how old the towns are

3. An oyster's chances of maturing are—
   (A) about even
   (B) very good
   (C) one in a million
   (D) more than one in a million

4. Perhaps it would be better—
   (A) to change our work hours
   (B) to work more slowly
   (C) for everyone to sleep in caves
   (D) to sleep longer

5. From the story we can tell that—
   (A) English wool is superior
   (B) wool was vital to the English economy
   (C) English laws have always been mild
   (D) there was little demand for wool in 1826

1.   We usually picture raindrops as tear-shaped—round on the bottom but curving gracefully to a pointed top. The laws of science dictate otherwise. The elastic surface of a raindrop seeks its most economical shape. As you may have learned from geometry, a sphere (a perfect ball) has less surface area for its volume than any other shape. So the most economical shape for a raindrop is a sphere.

2.   What creature could be more horrible than the basilisk? So dreadful was this legendary monster that it was said to kill with just a glance. Described as a snake with a human head, the basilisk was supposed to be hatched from an egg by a toad. The sight of a basilisk was so dreadful that if the creature saw its own reflection it would die of fright.

3.   Some people might admire an animal called the sloth. Since it is extremely slow and not very smart, you might expect that it is easily caught by larger animals. The opposite is true. The sloth hangs upside down in trees and moves so slowly that its enemies often do not notice it. Because sloths survive this way, their species has managed to stay on earth for millions of years.

4.   In the early 1800s, a Dr. Mitchell suggested that our country be called Fredonia. The scholarly doctor chose the beginning of the English word *freedom* and the ending of the Latin word *colonia*, meaning colony. Thus, *Fredonia* meant a free settlement or colony. The people of Dr. Mitchell's time didn't seem to like the doctor's new name for our country. As every-one knows, America never became known as Fredonia.

5.   The deep snow of winter may mean danger for people who live near rivers. To warn people who live where floods are likely, scientists study the snowy land using photographs taken from satellites. The photos measure the depth and area of the snow. From these measurements, scientists deter-mine how much flooding will follow the spring thaw.

1. Raindrops are not cube-shaped because—

   (A) **cubes have pointed tops**
   (B) **cubes don't bounce**
   (C) **cubes are not economical**
   (D) **raindrops are tear-shaped**

2. Basilisks would probably have to be most careful of—

   (A) **people with weapons**
   (B) **smooth, still water**
   (C) **toads**
   (D) **snakes**

3. If sloths moved faster, they might now be—

   (A) **right side up**
   (B) **rulers of the forest**
   (C) **extinct**
   (D) **far greater in number**

4. We know that Americans didn't like the name *Fredonia* because they—

   (A) **didn't understand Latin**
   (B) **kept the name *America***
   (C) **didn't want freedom**
   (D) **disliked Dr. Mitchell**

5. The paragraph leads you to understand that—

   (A) **in the future, floods may cause more damage**
   (B) **satellite photos serve as flood warnings**
   (C) **satellites can predict the hour a flood will start**
   (D) **winter is the most dangerous season for floods**

1.   In ancient Egypt, cats were worshipped as gods. Egyptians who harmed cats were punished. If an Egyptian killed a cat, the punishment was usually death. Owners of dead cats shaved off their own eyebrows as a sign of mourning. Dead cats were made into mummies. Egyptians even tucked mummified mice into the tomb so that their cats would not be hungry in "cat heaven."

2.   Thousands of people who cannot hear learn to read lips. Even people who use hearing aids find that knowing how to lipread helps tremendously. In lipreading courses, tongue and teeth positions are studied. The sounds, not the spellings, of the words are lipread. People are given lists of words with certain sounds to practice in front of a mirror. Good lipreaders never stop practicing.

3.   One of the oldest of Roman roads was made because of people's desire for salt. This road, the Via Salaria, or salt road, ran westward from Rome to the salt beds of Ostia on the coast of Italy. Salt was carried along this ancient road. It was this "white salary" that was given as an allowance to each soldier in the army of ancient Rome. In fact, this is how the word *salary* and the expression "worth one's salt" originated.

4.   The combination lock found on modern safes is old indeed. It was invented by the Chinese thousands of years ago. The lock consisted of a number of movable rings. Each ring was covered with letters. To open the lock, it was necessary to arrange the rings so that the letters spelled out a word that had been decided on in advance.

5.   Not many years ago, almost all medicines had a bad taste. It seemed to most people that the taste of the medicine was as unpleasant as the sickness it was designed to cure. Today most medicines have a pleasing artificial flavor that can hide a bad one. Some have a cherry taste. Sometimes the same medicine is manufactured in different flavors.

1. In ancient Egypt it is likely that most cats—

    (A) died young
    (B) lived long, happy lives
    (C) worked hard
    (D) had no eyebrows

2. You can tell that lipreading—

    (A) is exactly like a hearing aid
    (B) can be learned by almost anyone willing to practice
    (C) can be learned only by those who cannot hear others speak
    (D) has to do with the spellings of the words

3. You can tell that salt was used—

    (A) as medicine
    (B) as money
    (C) only in Ostia
    (D) only in eastern Italy

4. The Chinese invented—

    (A) the padlock
    (B) secret codes
    (C) the combination lock
    (D) the movable ring

5. We know that today—

    (A) all medicines taste bad
    (B) all medicines taste good
    (C) all medicines come in many flavors
    (D) medicines have changed

1.   You may like to care for an injured canary or bluebird, but what about an eagle or a falcon? The Troy Aviary in Utah has one of the few aid stations in this country for birds of prey—large birds with sharp claws for catching and eating small animals. The aviary fixes these birds' broken bones, cleans their wounds, and feeds them vitamins.

---

2.   Varnish is a liquid used to protect wooden surfaces from the damaging effects of air and moisture. Varnish also improves the appearance of a surface by giving it a smooth and glossy finish. Well-applied coats have been known to remain smooth and unscratched for centuries. Egyptian rulers' mummy cases, removed from ancient tombs, remain almost unchanged three thousand years after varnish was applied.

---

3.   The Romans thought highly of chickens for all important matters. A priest would write the letters of the alphabet on the ground in a circle and place a grain of wheat on each letter. Then a chicken was put in the center. The priest carefully watched from which letters the chicken took the wheat grains, and "read" the bird's choices as good or bad signs.

---

4.   What standard is used to set clocks in the United States? In the Naval Observatory Building near Washington, D.C., is a master clock. It is located in an airtight, dustproof, glass-enclosed chamber. The floor is eight inches thick so that nothing will jar the clock. All clocks in the United States are set from this master clock.

---

5.   Hundreds of years ago a man named Réaumur noticed that wasps' nests were made of a fine gray paper. He discovered that wasps chewed on bits of rotten wood. They mixed the bits of wood fiber with chemicals in their saliva. From this wood pulp the wasps made paper nests. Réaumur had discovered the wasps' secret—that paper could be made from wood without the use of rags.

1. You can tell that the Troy Aviary—

(A) is in a large city

(B) takes care of canaries and bluebirds

(C) takes care of creatures that kill

(D) is a zoo

2. One of the most important things about varnish is its—

(A) long-lasting quality

(B) variety of colors

(C) stickiness

(D) cheapness

3. You can tell that—

(A) chance played a major role in important Roman matters

(B) all the letters were the same

(C) the chicken learned to read the letters

(D) the Romans were the most superstitious of all people

4. The author implies that—

(A) clocks are easily thrown off time

(B) dust is good for clocks

(C) clocks must be set on a level floor

(D) little use is made of the master clock

5. From the story you can tell that—

(A) Mr. Réaumur was observant

(B) wasps are the same as bees

(C) Mr. Réaumur was a beekeeper

(D) paper is manufactured with saliva

1. English women once thought they looked best with wigs that rose two or even three feet above their heads. They certainly looked taller. Wool, cotton, and goats' hair were used to give the hairpieces the desired height. The finest high-piled wigs were often decorated with imitation fruit, model ships, horses, and figurines.

2. Though Americans take pride in the accomplishments of the pony express, few people know of an earlier and equally remarkable postal service. Eight hundred years before the pony express operated, messages traveled 150 miles a day—without the aid of a horse! Inca Indian runners were spaced about three miles apart over a stone road that stretched five thousand miles. These relay runners were the "express mail" carriers of their time.

3. When a large number of soldiers march across a small bridge, they are usually told to break step. If the bridge isn't particularly strong and the soldiers march in step, they can start a vibration that can cause the bridge to collapse. That is also the main reason why trains go slowly across bridges. A faster motion could set up vibrations and increase the danger of a bridge disaster.

4. The liver is the largest of the body's glands. It helps the body absorb food by producing a fluid that breaks down the food taken into the body. The liver keeps a close watch on the bloodstream, clearing the blood of many harmful products it can absorb. The liver also stores sugar for future use and makes sure that the heart does not become overloaded with blood.

5. By actually fishing for and catching other fish, the angler fish grows to be almost four feet long. It lies quietly in mud at the bottom of the water. Three wormlike "fingers" on the top of its head attract other fish. When the fish come close, the angler fish gets its meal. If fishing is slow, the angler fish may rise to the surface and swallow ducks, loons, or even geese.

1. From the story you cannot tell—
   (A) how wigs were decorated
   (B) how high the wigs were
   (C) what the wigs were made of
   (D) the color of the wigs

2. The best nickname for these Indian messengers would be—
   (A) Pony Express
   (B) Inca Express
   (C) Eight-hundred-year Mail
   (D) Horseless Carriage

3. Trains go slowly across bridges—
   (A) because bridges are long
   (B) because trains are long
   (C) for more than one reason
   (D) because most bridges are weak

4. The liver performs—
   (A) one function
   (B) two functions
   (C) four functions
   (D) three functions

5. You can conclude that angler fish—
   (A) prefer fish to other animals
   (B) have worms growing out of their heads
   (C) are often eaten by birds
   (D) always remain at the bottom of the water

The First L A P
Language Activity Pages

A. Exercising Your Skill

Do you enjoy riddles? Did you ever stop to think that when you solve a riddle, you are really **drawing a conclusion**? A conclusion is a decision or judgment you make based on facts and information. Read the following riddles and think about the information each one contains. Write the answers on your paper.

1. Do you say, "Seven and five is thirteen," or "Seven and five are thirteen"?
2. If you were hiking along a mountain trail in western Canada and saw a grizzly bear waking up from a long nap, what time would it be?
3. What was the highest mountain before Mt. Everest was discovered?
4. What is as big as an elephant but doesn't weigh anything?
5. Which month is the shortest?
6. Where can you always find health, wealth, and happiness?
7. What has a head but no brain?
8. What word is always pronounced incorrectly?
9. What can you add to a bucket of water that will make it weigh less?
10. How can you go without sleep for seven days and not get tired?

B. Expanding Your Skill

Take turns asking and answering the riddles. Did everyone come up with the same answers? Discuss the information given in each riddle that led to your answers. Then turn this page upside down to check the answers to the riddles.

Answers: 1. *Neither. Seven and five are twelve;* 2. *time to run;* 3. *Mt. Everest;* 4. *the elephant's shadow;* 5. *May;* 6. *in the dictionary;* 7. *lettuce, cabbage, cauliflower;* 8. *the word "incorrectly";* 9. *holes;* 10. *sleep at night*

C. Exploring Language

What makes a joke funny? To understand the humor of a joke, you need to draw conclusions about it. Read each of the following jokes. On your paper, answer the questions about the jokes.

1. Jan asked her teacher, "Would you scold someone for something she didn't do?" "Of course not," her teacher answered. "Why do you ask?" "Because I didn't do my math homework," Jan answered.

   What did the teacher mean when she said that she wouldn't scold someone for something she didn't do? Tell the class.

2. A traveler asked the ticket agent at a railroad station for a round trip ticket. "Where to?" the ticket agent asked. "Back to here," the traveler said.

   What did the ticket agent want to know? Tell the class.

3. Willy asked Billy, "Were you born in New York?" "Yes," Billy answered. "What part?" asked Willy. "All of me," said Billy.

   What did Willy want to know? Tell the class.

D. Expressing Yourself

Choose one of these activities.

1. Create riddles of your own to ask your classmates. See whether they can guess the answers to your riddles by using the information you provide. Have them explain how they arrived at the answers.

2. Play "Twenty Questions" with your classmates. The leader thinks of an object. The others ask questions that can be answered only by *yes* or *no*. Then they put the clues together to draw a conclusion about the object.

3. Tell jokes to the rest of the class. If you don't know any jokes, you can find them in a library book. Have your classmates tell what is funny about the jokes.

1.   The city of Minneapolis was named by a Mr. Hoag. In 1852, this little frontier village needed a name. Mr. Hoag decided to take the Indian word for the nearby falls, *Minnehaha*, and combine it with the Greek word *polis*, meaning city. He put them together, made some changes, and created *Minneapolis*. The name caught on with the settlers.

2.   Tinkers are people who wander the roads of Ireland. These gypsylike people travel in horse-drawn, covered wagons that hold all their possessions. At night, they camp by the roadside. Sometimes they do odd jobs. Sometimes they trade or sell odds and ends to villagers and passersby. Then off they go, once again, in whatever direction the roads want to take them.

3.   A train that flies two white flags is not a regularly scheduled train. It is an "extra" and is not on the railroad timetable. At night, white lights are used in place of the flags. If green flags or lights are used, the train is traveling in two sections, and the second section is following right behind.

4.   The expensive wedding gifts received by brides often attract thieves to the brides' homes. Since thieves can steal the presents most easily while the family is attending the wedding or its rehearsal, these criminals read the society pages of newspapers to find out brides' names and the times and places of marriage ceremonies.

5.   If somebody asked you, "What animal might you see climbing a coconut tree?" you would probably answer, "A monkey." However, you would be just as correct if you answered, "A crab." The large robber crab climbs coconut trees by wrapping its long legs around the trunk.

1. The word *Minneapolis*—

    (A) came about by pure chance
    (B) was liked by the Indians
    (C) came from two languages
    (D) is less than a hundred years old

---

2. You can tell that the tinkers—

    (A) aren't very clever
    (B) wander about aimlessly
    (C) have a fixed schedule
    (D) stay in one place

---

3. From the story you can't tell—

    (A) why the train is special
    (B) whether the train is regularly scheduled
    (C) what the color green means
    (D) what is used at night

---

4. You can tell that society pages contain—

    (A) names of criminals
    (B) information about weddings
    (C) lists of brides' gifts
    (D) prices of brides' gifts

---

5. From the story you cannot tell—

    (A) whether robber crabs can live outside of water
    (B) whether robber crabs eat coconuts
    (C) how robber crabs climb trees
    (D) whether robber crabs are large

1. Many blind people acquire information by listening to recordings. A new invention will help them speed up their learning. An electronic speech compressor can now reproduce human speech at roughly three hundred words a minute, which is double the normal speed. It does this without the distortion, or so-called "Donald Duck effect," that results from merely speeding up a recording.

2. Berries called rose hips became an important food in Great Britain during World War II. At that time, oranges and lemons—a major source of vitamin C for the British people—were in short supply. Rose hips, however, were rich in vitamin C and were available. The government encouraged the manufacture and sale of rose hip syrup, a product that is still sold today.

3. Chimpanzees are intrigued by watches and clocks. They enjoy holding a clock up to their ear and listening to it tick. This interest is so strong that chimps have been known to pick up a picture of a clock from a magazine and try to listen to it. On occasion, when holding a clock that starts to ring, they flee in panic!

4. Canada is rich in natural resources. About one-sixth of its land is suitable for farming. Canadian fishing grounds are extremely productive. Canada is among the chief producers of lead, zinc, copper, gold, nickel, and uranium. With a vast forest area covering nearly one million square miles, and a wealth of fur-bearing animals, Canada relies on its natural resources for a large portion of the country's exports.

5. Hummingbirds must eat almost constantly to live. Once, seven hummingbirds shipped to New York were sped by taxi to the Bronx Zoo. It was only a half-hour trip, but it proved too long for the hungry birds. By the time they reached the zoo, five had become unconscious from hunger, and one had died.

1. The normal speed of speaking—

   (A) can never be figured

   (B) is less than three hundred words a minute

   (C) is three hundred words a minute

   (D) is more than three hundred words a minute

2. The story shows that the British government was—

   (A) eager to make money

   (B) afraid of losing the war

   (C) unwilling to import oranges and lemons

   (D) concerned about its citizens' health

3. You can tell that chimpanzees—

   (A) recognize timepieces

   (B) are interested in time

   (C) can tell time

   (D) are mystified by time

4. The story mentions—

   (A) no resources

   (B) six metals

   (C) twelve major resources

   (D) twenty major resources

5. The hummingbirds were rushed to the zoo because—

   (A) it was late

   (B) they were ill

   (C) the zoo was closing

   (D) they needed to be fed

1.　The willow grows better beside America's rivers than any other kind of tree. The Mississippi River is bordered by willows for a distance of more than 2,500 miles. Dwarf willows grow well along mountain streams and along riverbanks in the dry plains of the West. These trees can live with their roots unprotected by soil. Willows that tumble into rivers and wash downstream can even put down their roots and grow again.

2.　Bees have cleanup squads that not only clean the wax cells that will hold the precious honey, but also help keep infection from spreading in another way. When a bee has died inside the hive, the workers carry the dead bee far away. In the case of larger animals who have died in the hive, they seal them in bee glue like mummies, thus preventing the spread of disease.

3.　During World War I, soldiers made use of avalanches. They turned them into weapons to be used against their enemies. The soldiers would fire into the snowy slopes directly above the enemy's position. The vibration would send tons of snow hurtling down the slopes, burying equipment and snuffing out the lives of their enemies with the "White Death," as effectively as thousands of sharpshooters.

4.　The first national park to be established in the United States east of the Mississippi River is known as Acadia National Park. The park, located in Maine, covers over 41,000 acres on Mount Desert Island, Isle au Haut, and on Schoodic Peninsula. A spectacular view is provided from the peak of Mount Cadillac. Acadia National Park is also an excellent sanctuary for wildlife.

5.　Moths are terrified by bats. This was discovered at a garden party one evening. A guest rubbed a cork against the rim of a wineglass. It gave forth a high-pitched squeak, much like the sound of a bat. Instantly, moths dropped to the ground as if shot. Only when they were convinced that everything was all right did they venture back into the air!

1. From the paragraph you can tell—

   (A) the height of a willow tree

   (B) where willow trees grow well

   (C) the shape of a willow tree

   (D) where willow trees are never found

2. Bees are very much concerned with their—

   (A) color

   (B) flowers

   (C) mummies

   (D) health

3. Soldiers of World War I apparently—

   (A) knew something about avalanches

   (B) were ignorant about avalanches

   (C) were mostly sharpshooters

   (D) were not armed with rifles

4. The writer hints that—

   (A) Mount Cadillac was named after an automobile

   (B) Acadia was America's first national park

   (C) earlier parks were established west of the Mississippi

   (D) there is little animal life in the park

5. You can tell how—

   (A) moths don't like high-pitched sounds

   (B) moths escape bats

   (C) moths like bats

   (D) bats fool moths

1.   In 1855, a Worcester, Massachusetts, inventor built a steam-powered organ. Its music could be heard ten miles away. The inventor decided to call this wonderful organ a calliope. *Kalliope*, in Greek, means "beautiful-voiced." Today, we can still hear the calliope at carnivals and fairs. The sound may not always be beautiful, but no one can say that it isn't loud and different.

2.   "Red sky in the morning, sailors take warning" is an old proverb that warns of rain. Actually, there is a reason why this proverb about the color of the morning sky was so widespread. A red sun indicates that there is dust and moisture in the air. These are two of the important elements necessary for rain. Thus, there is some degree of truth in the proverb.

3.   The Charter Oak was a famous tree in Hartford, Connecticut. In 1687 the government of England appointed an administrator to take away the charter and freedom of the Connecticut colony. According to tradition, the charter was hidden in an oak tree to keep the English from seizing it. Years later, winds destroyed this huge tree. Today, a monument marks the spot where the tree stood.

4.   Most snow avalanches make very little noise as they hurtle down mountainsides. Only a slight hissing sound can be heard. Large chunks of snow, however, make a dull, thudding sound as they go over cliffs. An ice avalanche has a sharper sound, more like thunder. An airborne powder avalanche, on the other hand, hums and whistles and whines as it makes its descent.

5.   In 1930, a German glider pilot jumped from his plane. Instead of falling, he was carried upward into a freezing mist that enclosed him in a huge chunk of ice. Eventually, the weight of the ice overcame the upward sweep of air. As the human hailstone fell, the ice melted, and the pilot's parachute opened. The pilot survived to tell the story.

1. You can tell that the inventor—

   (A) didn't take long to build the calliope

   (B) must have been deaf

   (C) liked the sound the calliope made

   (D) was a very musical person

---

2. You can tell that—

   (A) there is no truth to this proverb

   (B) other elements are also important for rain

   (C) rain doesn't need moisture or dust

   (D) sailors like red in the morning

---

3. A good name for the Charter Oak would be—

   (A) Yum-Yum Tree

   (B) Old Oaken Bucket

   (C) Freedom's Friend

   (D) Friendly Chestnut Tree

---

4. During a snow avalanche, people—

   (A) hear a great amount of noise

   (B) hear no sound at all

   (C) most likely hear a hissing sound

   (D) most likely hear a thunderous sound

---

5. From the story you can tell that—

   (A) the air grew warmer as the pilot fell

   (B) the pilot's plane was under attack

   (C) the incident occurred in Germany

   (D) the pilot reached the ground with no injuries

1. Who can hear higher sounds—men or women? If you guessed women, you were right. They can hear about an octave higher than men. Scientists say that there is a reason why women have a higher hearing range. In general, women seem to respond better to low-energy, high-frequency sounds.

2. Can volcanoes affect our weather? In 1815, a huge volcano erupted in the Java Sea. The next summer was an unusually cold one in North America, and people were puzzled by the low temperatures. Today many scientists think they know what happened. They believe that dust from the volcano spread into the atmosphere, screened the sun, and prevented its heat from reaching the earth.

3. Rats destroy buildings by digging beneath the foundations. The weakened buildings collapse. Rats cause floods by digging through dams. They have been known to start fires by gnawing through the protective covering of electric wires. By running across open switches and creating short circuits, rats have brought telephone communication to a halt.

4. The polar bear is one of the cleverest hunters in the animal kingdom. It will swim beneath the ice to a place near a seal's escape hole. The bear then raps on the underside of the ice. Alarmed, the seal dives into the water. Waiting for it is the crafty and hungry bear!

5. There aren't many date groves in the United States. It is more profitable to use land for houses and factories. However, there are a few groves in Arizona and Southern California. The National Date Festival, which originated in Indio, California, attracts about 200,000 visitors each year during the third week of February. There are camel races, horse shows, and many date-flavored foods, such as ice cream and milk shakes.

1. From the story you can tell—

    (A) which women can hear better
    (B) that women hear higher sounds
    (C) what an octave is
    (D) which sex has bigger ears

2. The story suggests that the connection between volcanoes and weather—

    (A) is based on a legend
    (B) became clear in 1815
    (C) is likely but not certain
    (D) may explain all unusual weather

3. The story mentions—

    (A) one way rats help us
    (B) two ways rats cause trouble
    (C) six ways rats cause trouble
    (D) four ways rats cause trouble

4. The writer suggests that the polar bear—

    (A) knows the habits of the seal
    (B) digs escape holes for seals
    (C) is the biggest animal
    (D) is a better swimmer than a seal

5. From the story you cannot tell—

    (A) why there are few date groves in the U.S.
    (B) when the date festival occurs
    (C) where most date groves are
    (D) how many dates are sold

1.   If you were trying to fall asleep, would a dark, quiet room be the best place to go? French scientists have found that a boring situation brings on sleep better than darkness and silence. In this experiment, people who experienced the tiresome repeating of a sound or light fell asleep more easily than people in quiet darkness. Next time you can't get to sleep, listen to the faucet drip or watch the corner traffic light.

---

2.   Almost no plants can survive in the bone-dry soil of Africa's Sahara desert. Yet, cave paintings created six thousand years ago in southern Algeria show farmers grazing cattle on rich grasslands. Changes in climate and the failure of people to be careful of soil and water supplies turned the pastureland to desert. The Sahara continues to spread southward each year.

---

3.   For the most part, soldiers who fought in the Civil War had no means of identification. Before some battles, soldiers made their own identification tags. Before especially dangerous attacks, some Union soldiers cut slips of paper and pinned them to the backs of their coats, so that their dead bodies could be identified when the battle was over.

---

4.   Some of the tricks played by tornadoes seem unbelievable. One tornado whisked all the feathers from a chicken, leaving the animal embarrassed but otherwise unharmed. Another snatched the covers off a surprised sleeper. Still other tornadoes have carried mirrors for miles, leaving them undamaged, without as much as a single crack!

---

5.   Few animals can leap like the kangaroo. A full-grown kangaroo can make jumps of twenty feet when it is in flight. It can also clear fences eight feet high. Even when an enemy catches up with it, the kangaroo is a difficult opponent. The kangaroo is also an excellent boxer, using its front paws. Its powerful tail can cause great damage, too.

1. People trying to stay awake should—

    (A) watch a slowly blinking light
    (B) listen to a repeated sound
    (C) read an exciting book
    (D) read a dull book

2. The writer does not suggest that—

    (A) cave paintings give information about the past
    (B) more rain used to fall in the region of the Sahara
    (C) southern Algeria is in the Sahara desert
    (D) people can change the Sahara back to farmland

3. You can tell that—

    (A) all soldiers always expected to die
    (B) many soldiers thought they might be killed
    (C) no soldiers thought that they would be killed
    (D) soldiers didn't want anyone to know who they were

4. You can tell that tornadoes—

    (A) don't occur very often
    (B) are more harmful than playful
    (C) never do any harm
    (D) play freakish tricks

5. The number of defenses listed for a kangaroo is—

    (A) two
    (B) three
    (C) four
    (D) five

A. Exercising Your Skill

An **analogy** is a way of comparing things. When we make an analogy, we are saying that things that are otherwise unlike *are* similar in some way. We are pointing out a relationship between two sets of things. For example:

Pitcher is to **baseball** as **quarterback** is to **football**.

In other words, a pitcher is one of the players in a baseball game, just as a quarterback is one of the players in a football game.

Analogies may show many different kinds of relationships. They may relate words with similar meanings (synonyms), words with opposite meanings (antonyms), parts to the whole, users to things used, or actions to objects.

Read each item below and draw a conclusion about the relationship between the sets of things. Ask yourself whether there is a relationship between the two sets of things. For each analogy, write *sense* or *no sense* on your paper to tell whether you think the analogy makes sense.

1. The **moon** is to the **earth** as the **earth** is to the **sun**.
2. **Puzzle** is to **solution** as **lock** is to **key**.
3. **Needles** are to **pine tree** as **leaves** are to **autumn**.
4. **Reality** is to **fantasy** as **pleasure** is to **enjoyment**.
5. **Gray** is to **black** as **pink** is to **red**.
6. **Ship** is to **port** as **car** is to **garage**.
7. **Row** is to **boat** as **pedal** is to **bicycle**.
8. **Fox** is to **den** as **grizzly** is to **bear**.
9. **Pod** is to **pea** as **shell** is to **walnut**.
10. **Scissors** are to **sharp** as **stapler** is to **staple**.

B. Expanding Your Skill

Discuss the analogies with your classmates. For each analogy that made sense, explain the relationship between the two sets of things. For each analogy that did not make sense, explain why there is no relationship. Then rewrite the incorrect analogies so that they make sense.

C. Exploring Language

To supply the missing word in an analogy, draw a conclusion about the relationship between the words in the complete pair. Then supply a word that has the same relationship to the remaining word. Remember that the relationship between the words in each pair must be similar, and the items in each pair must be in the same order.

Read each of the following incomplete analogies. On your paper, write the word that correctly completes each analogy.

1. **Valuable** is to **precious** as **worthless** is to _____ .
2. **Poodle** is to _____ as **Siamese** is to **cat**.
3. _____ is to **firefighter** as **hammer** is to **carpenter**.
4. **Numbers** are to **mathematics** as _____ are to **language**.
5. **Above** is to _____ as **front** is to **back**.
6. **Strings** are to **guitar** as _____ are to **piano**.
7. **Flock** is to **geese** as _____ is to **horses**.
8. _____ is to **state** as **state** is to **country**.
9. **Fawn** is to **deer** as _____ is to **cow**.
10. **Rainbow trout** is to _____ as **eagle** is to **bird**.

D. Expressing Yourself

Choose one of these activities.

1. Create your own analogies based on your favorite television or story characters, athletes, or entertainers from television, music, or movies. Share your analogies with your classmates. Be sure you can explain the relationships within the analogies.

2. Write an analogy of your own based on each kind of relationship listed below. Look back at analogies in Part C for examples if you need help.

   1. antonyms
   2. item to category
   3. part to whole
   4. synonyms
   5. animal to its young

1. Often the history of a word gives a clue to its meaning, but sometimes the original meaning no longer applies. Back in Roman times, four of the months were named for the order in which they occurred. *September*, *October*, *November*, and *December* meant "seventh," "eighth," "ninth," and "tenth." As you can tell, the names have been kept, but our calendar has changed.

2. Many people mistakenly think that a camel's hump is used to store water for long desert travel. This is not true. Camels' humps are food storehouses. They are made of fat, which is stored energy, just as in human bodies. When other food sources are scarce, a camel can absorb energy from its hump. As it does so, the hump shrinks.

3. Earthquakes are often classified into three groups. Normal or shallow earthquakes, which originate somewhere between the earth's surface and forty-four miles beneath, are the most common type. Quakes that start between forty-four and 188 miles beneath the surface are classified as intermediate earthquakes. Those that originate deeper than 188 miles are called deep earthquakes.

4. In the southern United States during early colonial days, there were very few towns and thus, very few inns. Travelers didn't have many places to stay. Planters, separated by great distances from their neighbors, led lonely lives. They were always glad to see new faces. Sometimes they would station servants at places where a traveler might pass, to extend an invitation for a meal or a night's lodging.

5. The Merino sheep is a champion producer of wool. It is covered with fleece from its nose to its tail. A large Merino may produce as much as thirty pounds of wool. This is enough to make cloth for eleven high-quality woolen suits. The amount of wool from the shearing of one Merino ram, spun into a single thread, would stretch from Chicago to New York!

1. The Roman year must have begun in—

   (A) June
   (B) August
   (C) March
   (D) February

---

2. You can conclude from the information that—

   (A) a camel's hump expands when it eats
   (B) a camel's hump shrinks when the camel is thirsty
   (C) camels never need to drink water at all
   (D) camels can only find food in the desert

---

3. Earthquakes are often classified by—

   (A) the amount of damage they cause
   (B) their point of origin
   (C) their noise
   (D) their size

---

4. Planters of early colonial times probably—

   (A) were afraid
   (B) were self-sufficient
   (C) were often alone
   (D) had many friends

---

5. From the story you can't tell—

   (A) what is made from Merino wool
   (B) why the Merino is a champion wool producer
   (C) why Merino sheep are valued
   (D) how much the Merino weighs

1. In an old-time "aerodrome" in Old Rhinebeck, New York, people can imagine themselves back in World War I. Small wood-and-wire planes buzz skyward to act out the air fights of 1917. These creations look fragile compared with today's jets, but their ability to move about easily is amazing. One plane dives straight down at another, which suddenly dips and slips away sideways. Monoplanes, biplanes, and triplanes are kept here in perfect working condition.

2. There is no such thing as a perfect clock. Some run fast and others slow. But the closest thing to perfection is the atomic clock. It is so accurate that scientists predict it will lose only one second in 200,000 years. Unfortunately, it is not for sale at the corner store. This clock is designed for scientific use and costs over fifty thousand dollars!

3. Certain hurricanes are called "hundred-year-storms," meaning that they are predicted to happen only once each century. Hurricanes Hugo and Andrew, in 1989 and 1992, were both "hundred-year-storms." Meteorologists wonder what is happening. They suspect that global warming, which is the result of increased burning of fossil fuels, may be making storms more violent.

4. People drive long distances to see the Painted Desert in Arizona. The desert is best viewed at sunrise and sunset, when the colors are the most brilliant and the shadows the deepest. Minerals in the sand reflect the sun's rays and make the Painted Desert one of the most exciting sights in all the Southwest.

5. Anagrams are made by rearranging the letters in a word or group of words so that they spell a different word or phrase. The letters can be arranged in any order, not just reversed. For example, the letters in the word "rat" may be rearranged to spell "tar." An anagram for astronomer could be "moon starer."

1.   You can tell that in 1917—

(A) travel by airplanes was common
(B) airplanes were better than modern jets
(C) World War I was being fought
(D) a battle was fought at the aerodrome

2.   The perfect clock—

(A) has not yet been invented
(B) is in common use
(C) can be purchased in the U.S.
(D) is the sundial

3.   You can conclude from the paragraph that—

(A) people are angry at weather predictions
(B) hurricanes Hugo and Andrew were a century apart
(C) global warming is caused by severe hurricanes
(D) meteorologists speculate about today's weather patterns

4.   The Painted Desert is probably most attractive—

(A) when it is cloudy
(B) at midday
(C) at twilight
(D) at midnight

5.   An example of a word and its anagram is—

(A) return - comeback
(B) sail - sole
(C) renew - newer
(D) small - tall

1.   A number of years ago the people of central California conducted a campaign against coyotes. Many coyotes were poisoned. Partly as a result of the near extermination of coyotes, who feed on mice, mice began to multiply rapidly. Millions swept over the countryside, over eighty thousand mice per acre, eating everything in their paths, including millions of dollars' worth of grain and other products.

2.   Mystic, Connecticut, is a rebuilt colonial seaport and ship-building center. Here at the river's edge you can see the *Charles W. Morgan*, the last remaining wooden whaling ship. You can also see the *Australia*, a seventy-five-foot, two-masted schooner that is the oldest American schooner afloat. The shops, stores, and cobblestone streets also help remind visitors of life during the days of the great sailing ships.

3.   In 279 B.C., a king named Pyrrhus won an important battle. The fight, however, cost him so many soldiers and officers that his army was seriously weakened. Joyless in his win, King Pyrrhus said, "One more such victory and we are lost." Indeed, in the end he lost the war. Today, such a victory is often called a "Pyrrhic victory."

4.   The unit used to measure distance traveled over water is called the nautical mile. It is equal to 6,076 feet. The statute mile, 5,280 feet, is a unit of land measurement. Clearly, the distance is not the same. When we use the word "mile," we should be certain that the listener knows which mile we are talking about.

5.   Women have long been skilled in the use of beauty aids. Cleopatra painted her eyebrows and lashes black, just as many women do today. She painted her upper lids blue-black and the lower ones green. Cleopatra was also familiar with cold cream, the oldest cosmetic known to history.

1. The people who exterminated so many coyotes—

   (A) must have regretted it
   (B) must have been very proud
   (C) were probably savages
   (D) were probably timid

2. The story hints that there may—

   (A) still exist a great number of schooners
   (B) soon be a second great age of sailing ships
   (C) be little interest in the port
   (D) still exist whaling ships made of other materials

3. A Pyrrhic victory is—

   (A) unexpected
   (B) not worth the price
   (C) won by accident
   (D) unfair

4. From the story you can tell that—

   (A) both miles are the same
   (B) the statute mile is longer
   (C) the nautical mile is longer
   (D) travel is faster on land

5. Women who use beauty aids do so mostly—

   (A) to cover flaws
   (B) to aid health
   (C) because Cleopatra did
   (D) to improve their appearance

UNIT 16

1. Ships that carry freight but do not travel on regular runs are called "tramps." A tramp steamer has no fixed schedule. It wanders from port to port. Declining in numbers in recent years, tramp steamers are less and less often seen. When the last of the tramp steamers has made its final port call, a little of the romance of the old sailing days will have vanished.

2. The rhinoceros is regarded by hunters as one of the most dangerous animals in the world. Despite its size, the animal gallops along at twenty-five to thirty-five miles an hour. Its horn gives it a formidable weapon. What is worse, the rhino has a mean temper. Without any apparent reason, the tanklike creature will attack even a railroad train!

3. Elephants display surprising intelligence. In the London Zoo elephants were separated from the public by two fences. Sometimes peanuts thrown by the onlookers landed between these fences, beyond the reach of both the people and the elephants. With a blast of air from their trunks, the elephants simply blew the peanuts back to the crowd so they could be tossed back again!

4. The English language did not originate in England. The language that became known as English was apparently first spoken by people living in what is now Germany. Tribes from this area brought their language with them when they invaded England. When we hear this early English, known as Anglo-Saxon or Old English, we find it hard to believe that it was the ancestor of Modern English. It sounds more like German.

5. The flu, or influenza, has been around for centuries. Its name reminds us that people once looked to the sky for its cause. The word *influenza* comes from the Italian word for *influence*, because people blamed their aches and fevers on the influence of the stars. In modern times, scientists have found a better explanation by looking through a microscope. The flu is caused by a tiny form of matter called a virus.

1. You can tell that the writer thinks that—

    (A) there will always be some tramp steamers

    (B) the end of tramp steamers is no loss

    (C) tramp steamers should have a schedule

    (D) tramp steamers will one day be no more

2. The story gives—

    (A) ten reasons why hunters fear the rhino

    (B) at least three reasons why the rhino is dangerous

    (C) the reason for the rhino's mean temper

    (D) a complete list of the rhino's habits

3. From the story you cannot tell—

    (A) where the elephants were kept

    (B) how many fences were there

    (C) how many peanuts were lost

    (D) how the elephants returned the peanuts

4. The writer suggests that without Germany—

    (A) there would be no written language

    (B) the English language would be different today

    (C) there would be no English people

    (D) England would have no language

5. From the story you can tell that—

    (A) a virus can be seen with the naked eye

    (B) the stars once caused sickness

    (C) the author believes in scientific explanations

    (D) a cure for the flu has been discovered

1. How hot a temperature can humans stand? A century ago, a French performer astonished audiences by remaining inside an iron closet heated to 220 degrees Fahrenheit for a half-hour. This same person once briefly endured 380 degrees—almost twice as hot as boiling water. More recently, air force volunteers wearing heavy clothing, in dry air, withstood five hundred degrees! The drier the air, the more heat a person can stand.

2. Some of the largest fires in history were started by seemingly insignificant accidents. In 1833, the great fire of New York City was started by stray sparks from a stove. By the time the fire was under control, seventeen entire blocks of the Wall Street area had been consumed. Six hundred buildings lay in ruins. The damage was estimated at fifteen million dollars.

3. Airplanes have rules that govern the right of way in the sky. If two planes are flying so that their paths cross, the plane to the right has the right of way. If two planes are about to meet head-on, both pilots must fly their planes to the right. Airplanes must always give gliders and balloons the right of way.

4. When in danger, the hedgehog can usually protect itself by rolling up into a tight ball. Completely surrounded by its own sharp spines, it is safe from most animals. A fox, however, may sometimes outsmart the hedgehog by rolling it into water. The hedgehog must then unroll itself in order to swim, leaving its underside open to attack by the fox.

5. On an island near Sicily there is a volcano named Stromboli. The island itself bears the same name. There is more affection for Stromboli than there is for the usual volcano. Stromboli erupts every few minutes, even on the darkest of nights. For thousands of years it has been a guide to ships at sea. It has rightfully earned the title "Lighthouse of the Mediterranean Sea."

UNIT 17

1. The 380-degree air around the French performer must have been—

    (A) air-conditioned
    (B) very moist
    (C) very dry
    (D) a false thermometer reading

2. You can tell that before the fire the Wall Street area contained—

    (A) few wooden buildings
    (B) many fire hydrants
    (C) few fire alarms
    (D) many wooden buildings

3. Air and auto traffic are alike because—

    (A) neither are dangerous
    (B) only single lane traffic is allowed
    (C) they both have traffic laws
    (D) each has speed laws

4. From the story you can tell that a hedgehog—

    (A) rolls into a ball to keep warm
    (B) uses its spines to threaten its enemies
    (C) is a poor swimmer
    (D) does not have spines on its underside

5. Stromboli is liked because it—

    (A) is a volcano
    (B) is nice and warm
    (C) is helpful
    (D) sends out lava

1.   Long ago, passenger pigeons flew over North America in such vast numbers that they actually darkened the sun as they passed. In a single flock there were often more than a billion passenger pigeons! Single nesting areas were often thirty or more miles long and three to six miles wide. Today, the passenger pigeon is extinct. The last survivor of the breed died in a Cincinnati zoo in 1914.

2.   In 1959, a British engineer invented a transportation machine called the hovercraft. It is a boat-shaped, flat-bottomed carrier that rides on a cushion of air created by motors. One special feature of the hovercraft is its ability to ride over both land and water at heights low enough for easy viewing. This has been useful in the exploration of swampy rivers such as the Amazon.

3.   The most beautiful of all horses is the Arabian Asil. Its neck is gracefully arched. Its head is small and delicate with eyes that are large, fiery, and far apart. Its small ears point inward. This horse has a full, flowing tail that it carries high, and its skin is a shiny black. The Arabian Asil is one of the most beautiful of all creatures.

4.   The area that birds defend against other birds of their own species is called a territory. By controlling such an area, the bird protects its family from other birds of the same species. It also insures both food and nesting materials in this way. The size of the territory depends on many factors, such as the amount of food available, the type of bird, and even its size.

5.   Down through the ages flea circuses have been used to attract people to fairs and markets. Fleas are dressed in tiny costumes. Some are tightrope walkers. Others take part in chariot races and tugs of war. Today, most of these circuses have disappeared. However, the name remains in the so-called flea market, an open-air market in which various goods are sold.

1. From the story you cannot tell—

    (A) how large the flocks were
    (B) when the passenger pigeon became extinct
    (C) why the passenger pigeon died out
    (D) where the last passenger pigeon died

2. From the story you can tell that the hovercraft—

    (A) could be used for exploring a chain of islands
    (B) resembles a helicopter
    (C) is unsafe in stormy weather
    (D) creates less noise and pollution than an automobile

3. A good name for the Arabian Asil would be—

    (A) Star of the North
    (B) Brown Eyes
    (C) Speedy
    (D) Black Beauty

4. The story gives—

    (A) ten reasons for bird territories
    (B) the writer's opinion of birds
    (C) three reasons for bird territories
    (D) the size of most bird territories

5. Fleas were helpful in—

    (A) scattering crowds
    (B) drawing crowds
    (C) annoying crowds
    (D) calming crowds

1.   Walking on the wing of an airplane in flight was all in a day's work to Mabel Cody. This star of an aerial circus wore no parachute. Graceful, sure-footed Mabel Cody stood on the top of the upper wing of an airplane. As the air blasted against her, Mabel gaily waved her arms to the crowds who gazed up at her in awe.

2.   The yo-yo, whose name means "come-come" or "to return," was first brought to the United States in the 1920s by a Philippine man named Pedro Flores. The yo-yo had already been a popular toy in the Philippines for many years. Flores settled in California and began carving yo-yos out of wood. Eventually, he started a yo-yo company.

3.   The world's highest waterfall is not Niagara Falls. The highest water-fall lies deep in the jungles of Venezuela and is more than one thousand feet higher than any other yet found. Named Angel Falls, after its American discoverer Jimmy Angel, the waterfall is almost a mile high. Its nearest competitor is the Kukenaam Falls, also in Venezuela.

4.   The rhinoceros, one of the world's most dangerous animals, gets along very well with a small bird that perches on its back. The bird, the oxpecker, eats insects from the back of the rhino. In exchange for its free meal the oxpecker acts as an early-warning system for the rhino. If the bird suddenly takes flight, the rhinoceros knows danger lurks nearby.

5.   Lacrosse is the oldest organized sport played in North America. This fast, rough game was played originally by Canadian Indians. Early French and English settlers, after watching the Indians play, adopted the game and made some changes in the rules. In modern lacrosse, players using long, net-ended sticks try to hurl or kick a ball into the opposing team's goal area.

1. You can tell that Mabel Cody—

    (A) had a good sense of balance

    (B) was rather cautious

    (C) loved all kinds of people

    (D) was insane

---

2. The story suggests that Pedro Flores—

    (A) invented the yo-yo

    (B) started the first American yo-yo company

    (C) had sold yo-yos in the Philippines before 1920

    (D) named the yo-yo

---

3. From the story you can tell that—

    (A) Niagara Falls is the world's third highest falls

    (B) Angel Falls is not as high as Kukenaam

    (C) Angel Falls is higher than Niagara or Kukenaam

    (D) Angel Falls is only one thousand feet high

---

4. The story tells—

    (A) four services the oxpecker provides

    (B) two services the oxpecker provides

    (C) the reasons why rhinos are dangerous

    (D) what danger exists for rhinos

---

5. From the story you can tell that—

    (A) lacrosse is North America's most popular game

    (B) early settlers learned from the Indians

    (C) no changes have ever been made in lacrosse

    (D) all people played lacrosse

A. Exercising Your Skill

A good detective uses clues to draw a conclusion about a crime. A good reader uses clues provided by the writer to draw a **conclusion** about a piece of writing. How good a detective are you? Read each of the sets of clues below. On your paper, write what you think happened in each case.

EVENT 1

Girl Scouts	tents	campfire
ghost stories	cold stream	sleeping bags
mosquitoes buzzing	moonless night	clearing in woods

What do you think happened? _____

EVENT 2

row of footprints	gray dust	silence
weightlessness	spacesuits	empty landscape
Earth shining above	rocks and craters	black sky

What do you think happened? _____

EVENT 3

crisp fall day	football field	teams running off
Visitors: 7	Home: 10	football held high
coach on shoulders	cheering crowd	banners waving

What do you think happened? _____

B. Expanding Your Skill

Compare the conclusions you drew about each event with your classmates' conclusions. Did everyone arrive at the same conclusions? Why or why not? Discuss the clues that led to each conclusion. What other clues might have helped you draw that conclusion? On your paper, write additions to the list for each event.

C. Exploring Language

On page 48, you drew conclusions about an event that was based on nine facts. Let's see how good you are at drawing conclusions based on just three facts! Read each of the following items. Based on the overheard bits of conversation, tell what is happening.

1. "Get those ladders up there!" "Hoses on!" "There are people on the top floor!"
2. "It's almost time for the show to start." "Look at that line at the ticket booth!" "Do you want to get some popcorn?"
3. "The Flying Estradas will now perform their own version of the triple somersault!" "Drum roll, please!" "He's going to fall! Oh, I can't bear to watch!"
4. "Forty-second Street. This station is Forty-second Street." "Excuse me. Coming through." "Watch your step, please, and stay clear of the track."
5. "Please deposit 25 cents for the next three minutes." "Operator, I have no more change!" "This is a recording."
6. "Come, Sandy." "Exercise over. You can praise your dog now." "Good boy, Sandy!"
7. "Look! Bases loaded!" "How many outs?" "Maybe she'll hit a grand slam homer!"
8. "Open your test booklets and begin." "Answer all the questions." "No talking!"

D. Expressing Yourself

Choose one of these activities.

1. Work together with a group of classmates to plan and act out a scene. (This can be one of the events based on the clues in Part C.) Have your other classmates draw a conclusion about what is happening. Ask them to explain their thoughts.

2. Make up a list of clues about an event. Then trade lists with a classmate. Write a few sentences that draw a conclusion about your classmate's list.

3. Write a short description of an area inside or near your school or of a well-known place in your town or city—but *don't* name it. Then exchange papers with a partner. Name the place your partner described. Was your guess correct? Did your partner guess correctly the place you described?

1.   In the early 1890s, a teacher named James Naismith was asked to think up an active game that could be played indoors during the winter. Taking ideas from a game called "Duck on a Rock," Naismith invented the first, rough version of basketball. The court was a YMCA gym with peach baskets nailed to the balcony. When a player made a basket, play would stop while someone climbed a ladder to take the ball out of the basket.

2.   The most unusual member of the deer family is the Florida Key deer. Even when fully grown, it is the world's smallest. Fires, hurricanes, and hunters have taken the lives of many of these deer. Their eating habits have further reduced their numbers. Their fondness for cigarette butts tempts the creatures onto the Key West Highway!

3.   Some birds have an amazing ability to find their eggs after a storm. Terns, for example, nest for the most part on sand, often laying two or three eggs in a shallow hole. Repeated observations have shown that even though the eggs are completely concealed by windblown sand, adult terns can easily find them.

4.   A fire extinguisher has been invented that can put out a fire very quickly. It works so fast that a piece of paper soaked in gasoline and lighted with a match won't even be scorched. The device automatically releases a gas that instantly breaks the chain reaction needed for combustion.

5.   Diamonds are now being mined from the ocean floor. A suction hose brings gravel to the surface. The yield is much greater than that on land. One carat in diamonds is obtained for each ton of gravel processed from the sea, compared with one carat for every twenty-three tons processed on land. Furthermore, the diamonds from the sea bed are of a higher quality.

1. From the story you cannot tell that—
    - **(A) basketball has changed since the first game**
    - **(B) the bottoms were not cut out of the first baskets**
    - **(C) basketball has been around for about a hundred years**
    - **(D) the walls of the gym were the first boundaries**

2. The writer suggests that—
    - **(A) the deer get sick**
    - **(B) people litter along the highway**
    - **(C) the deer love people**
    - **(D) the deer are moving North**

3. The story doesn't tell—
    - **(A) where terns lay eggs**
    - **(B) how many eggs terns lay**
    - **(C) how terns can find the eggs**
    - **(D) what windblown sand does to eggs**

4. A good name for the new extinguisher would be—
    - **(A) Blaze and Burn**
    - **(B) Gas and Oil**
    - **(C) Flame and Fire**
    - **(D) Fast and Out**

5. To produce one-carat's worth of diamonds from the ocean demands—
    - **(A) no processing**
    - **(B) more processing than on land**
    - **(C) just as much processing as on land**
    - **(D) less processing than on land**

1.   If you think life is tough, think of the mayfly. It exists undeveloped in the water for many months, perhaps a year. This length of time makes the mayfly's chances of being gobbled up by fish very great. The few mayflies that survive to leave the water might ask, "Was it worth it?" On land, the mayfly reaches adulthood, mates, lays its eggs, and dies—all within twenty-four hours!

2.   Soap is now considered a mark of cultured living. Important as soap is to us today, it was all but unknown until about two thousand years ago. Before people knew about soap, they scraped dirt from their bodies with twigs or an instrument known as a strigil. In still other times, people cleaned themselves with olive oil or plant juices.

3.   A virus is a microscopic organism that cannot do anything by itself. It has to invade a living cell, where it causes diseases such as the flu, a cold, or AIDS. Computer viruses are much the same. They can enter a computer and "infect" a program that is already running. Then they take over and cause trouble in the computer, just as illness causes trouble for humans.

4.   In the summer, you can find out the temperature without listening to the weather station or looking at a thermometer. Just go outside to a quiet place and listen to the crickets. Count the number of times the crickets chirp in fifteen seconds. Then add forty to that number. The sum will be very close to the actual temperature.

5.   Pound for pound, few creatures can match the appetite of the platypus of Australia. This strange creature looks like a combination of a muskrat and a duck. It weighs only two to four pounds. Yet it is so active that it must eat huge meals. In a single day it can devour a thousand earthworms and fifty crayfish!

1. The writer seems to feel that the mayfly's adult life is—

    (A) just like our lives
    (B) not worth the wait
    (C) worth waiting for
    (D) more exciting than ours

---

2. People of olden times—

    (A) were interested in cleanliness
    (B) took showers every day
    (C) didn't like soap
    (D) knew much about soap

---

3. You can conclude from this paragraph that—

    (A) computer viruses can cause AIDS
    (B) computer programmers often get the flu
    (C) computer viruses are living things
    (D) computer viruses are powerless by themselves

---

4. The story does not suggest that—

    (A) this method is used only in the summer
    (B) crickets chirp faster as the temperature rises
    (C) this method was used before thermometers existed
    (D) this method is not exact

---

5. The platypus has few rivals in—

    (A) intelligence
    (B) activity
    (C) beauty
    (D) appetite

UNIT 22

1. Try to imagine an Italian meal without tomato sauce. Yet, the tomato was once considered unsafe to eat by most people in Europe. They believed that tomatoes would chill the body and cause illness. Although South Americans had eaten tomatoes for centuries, Europeans planted them only for their beauty. In the 1800s, Europeans finally began using tomatoes as food.

---

2. Many people think that they know why leaves change color in the fall. They say it is because of frost. Actually, the color changes because of a reduced amount of sunlight. This means a slowdown in the production of chlorophyll, which is dark green. The less chlorophyll, the more other colors shine through.

---

3. One of the first elephants brought to America was "Old Bet." She arrived in the early 1800s. Her owner had paid $1,000 for her, and he did not want anyone to get a free look at his prize. He wanted to exhibit her for money. How did he solve his problem? He and "Old Bet" walked country roads at night so that no one could see them.

---

4. More than two million of the 2,700,000 soldiers in the Union army during the Civil War were twenty-one years old or younger. Over one million were eighteen. About 100,000 were fifteen or under. Three hundred were thirteen or under. These youngest were usually fifers and drummers, but sometimes they also fought.

---

5. Long before an earthquake occurs, many animals seem to sense its approach. Cattle and sheep refuse to enter their pens. Rats flee their homes and pigeons will not land. Fish leap above the surface of the water as if they would feel safer in the air. Even snakes that sleep through the winter wake up and leave their burrows. No one is sure what signals the animals to the danger.

1. You can tell that Europeans in the 1800s—

   (A) first began planting tomatoes
   (B) were introduced to tomatoes by South Americans
   (C) grew sick from eating tomatoes
   (D) learned that tomatoes were not unhealthful

2. The more chlorophyll there is in leaves, the—

   (A) more frost there is
   (B) less sunlight there is
   (C) greener they are
   (D) more quickly they change colors

3. You can tell that—

   (A) elephants were common in the eighteenth century
   (B) "Old Bet" would earn money as a curiosity
   (C) "Old Bet's" owner did not like people
   (D) people had seen many elephants

4. Most of the Union army soldiers were—

   (A) musicians
   (B) eighteen years old
   (C) under twenty-two years old
   (D) unreliable

5. From the story you cannot tell whether—

   (A) animals feel or hear earthquake vibrations
   (B) animals prefer open spaces before an earthquake
   (C) animal behavior can warn people of earthquakes
   (D) wild animals can sense approaching earthquakes

1.   On the island of Molokai in Hawaii there is a rubber-bottomed lake. It is a human-made lake to hold water for irrigating the fields where pineapple and other crops grow. Such a lake is called a reservoir. This reservoir had to have a huge rubber bottom put in. Otherwise the water would leak away into the ground. Now farmers on Molokai have enough water to raise good crops.

---

2.   In the early days of Texas, the famed longhorn cattle were worth more for hides than for meat. Rawhide provided a valuable building material in the old West. Hides were used in binding beams and fence rails, and in fastening furniture. Even items of clothing were made of rawhide—boots, shoes, trousers, and jackets. In the absence of other building materials, Texans and others had found a valuable substitute—rawhide.

---

3.   Hurricane hunters are always on the alert for those storms that whip out of the Caribbean with such destructive force. The hurricane hunters' planes circle the storm area, getting readings on the hurricane's size, its strength, and the direction in which it is moving. Small radio transmitters are dropped into the storm centers by parachute and relay important information back to the plane.

---

4.   Long ago there were not enough horses. People often rode in a "ride-and-tie" fashion. Two got on the horse, one behind the other while another couple walked. After a mile or two, the riders got off, tied the horse to a tree, and began to walk. The next couple, when they came to the horse, would ride a mile or two past the walking couple, tie up the horse, and start walking.

---

5.   The word *skate* is taken from a Dutch word meaning "leg bone." A Viking boot and skate from the tenth century have been found. The boot is not attached to the skate, however. The skater's weight probably kept the foot in place.

1. You can tell that this part of Molokai—

   (A) has many rubber trees
   (B) gets very heavy rainfall
   (C) gets only light rainfall
   (D) is below sea level

---

2. You can tell that the hides—

   (A) were expensive
   (B) had a good taste
   (C) had more uses than the meat
   (D) wore out quickly

---

3. Hurricane hunters must be—

   (A) strong
   (B) pilots
   (C) fighters
   (D) big

---

4. By using this method—

   (A) the horse got a ride
   (B) each person rode all the way
   (C) even the horse got a rest
   (D) each person walked all the way

---

5. This paragraph suggests that—

   (A) Vikings did not skate before the tenth century
   (B) today's skates should not be attached to shoes
   (C) the Dutch have no word for *boot*
   (D) the first materials used for skates were bones

1. Dinosaurs swallowed stones to help them digest their food. (Chickens do this also, but the stones they swallow are much smaller.) The juices inside the dinosaurs' stomachs made the stones smooth and shiny over a period of time. These stones are sometimes called gizzard stones or gastroliths. Naturally, they are prized by fossil collectors.

2. Those who want to learn more about the life of Helen Keller should visit Tuscumbia, Alabama, her birthplace. Each summer, William Gibson's play, *The Miracle Worker,* is staged there. This play dramatizes the story of Helen Keller, blind and deaf from the age of two. Her courage and the efforts of her teacher and companion, Anne Sullivan, provide audiences with an unforgettable experience.

3. The most famous rock in America lies on the seashore at Plymouth, Massachusetts, under the protection of a large granite canopy. According to tradition, the Pilgrims stepped from their ship, the *Mayflower*, onto this rock when they landed on December 21, 1620. Today, people come from all over America to see this famous rock, which stands as a symbol of the Pilgrims' courage.

4. In the Asian country of Sri Lanka, there is an orphanage for baby elephants. The babies are fed milk from a rubber hose that is attached to a bottle. Every morning, they walk down a path to the river, and children from the village walk along with them. At the river, the elephants bathe and play in the water.

5. One of the truly great agricultural expositions in America is held during August on a two-hundred-acre fairground in Des Moines, Iowa. The Iowa State Fair, which dates back over one hundred years, attracts half a million visitors annually. Young and old are enlightened and entertained by contests, demonstrations, agricultural and industrial exhibits, horse shows, auto races, and fireworks.

1. From the story you can tell—

    (A) that dinosaurs and chickens have nothing in common

    (B) why dinosaurs swallowed stones

    (C) that dinosaur meat was delicious

    (D) that the stones were swallowed by accident

---

2. The *Miracle Worker* is probably—

    (A) a long play

    (B) a dull play

    (C) an inspiring play

    (D) a three-act play

---

3. Plymouth Rock is—

    (A) larger than the *Mayflower*

    (B) a reminder of our history

    (C) not well known

    (D) a famous amusement center

---

4. From the story you cannot tell—

    (A) how the elephants are fed

    (B) what the elephants eat

    (C) how the elephants became orphans

    (D) that the elephants enjoy the river

---

5. From the story you can tell that—

    (A) the Iowa Fair is for Iowans only

    (B) the Iowa Fair appeals to different people

    (C) the Iowa Fair does not have exhibitions

    (D) farmers would not enjoy the Iowa Fair

1. One of our five senses needs help to work well. The tongue can sense only four tastes—sweet, sour, bitter, and salty. Taste alone cannot tell one sweet thing from another, such as a cookie from a lollypop. We depend also on what each looks like, smells like, and feels like in our mouth.

2. Inventors are often very observant. Percy Spencer was standing in front of a magnetron, an electronic tube that produces microwaves. It was developed during World War II for use in radar systems. A chocolate bar Spencer had in his pocket melted as he stood there, and he wondered if microwaves could be used for cooking. They could. The first such oven was patented in 1946.

3. People have been ice skating in northern Europe for over two thousand years. The earliest skate blades were made of animal bones. Later they were made of wood, then iron, and now steel. Ice skating first became really popular in the Netherlands. There the country's network of canals became highways of ice in the winter, and people could skate to work or school.

4. "To go highhat" means to become a snob and look down on your friends. Long ago, people who became suddenly wealthy often wore silly high hats. They ignored friends that they had when they were poor. Their high hats became signs of their new-found wealth. Thus arose the expression, "to go highhat."

5. The overland coaches that rolled across America in the early 1800s were not only fashioned with craftsmanship, but they were as attractive as they were sturdy. Pictures were painted on each door, most often landscapes or portraits of famous people. Even the wheels wore handsome stripes.

1. If you closed your eyes and held your nose, it would be hardest to tell the difference between swallowing—

    (A) **sugar and salt**
    (B) **canned pears and canned peaches**
    (C) **a pickle slice and a banana slice**
    (D) **grapefruit juice and pineapple juice**

---

2. You can conclude from this paragraph that—

    (A) **Percy Spencer was a war hero**
    (B) **Percy Spencer invented the chocolate bar**
    (C) **Percy Spencer invented the magnetron**
    (D) **Percy Spencer invented the microwave oven**

---

3. Skating became popular in the Netherlands because—

    (A) **the winters were so long and cold**
    (B) **skate blades had been improved**
    (C) **it was a handy means of transportation**
    (D) **the frozen canals made smooth skating surfaces**

---

4. People often "go highhat" because of—

    (A) **the poor**
    (B) **their friends**
    (C) **their neighbors**
    (D) **money**

---

5. You can tell that the overland coaches were—

    (A) **attractively designed**
    (B) **very roomy**
    (C) **often in need of repair**
    (D) **not often used**

A. Exercising Your Skill

A **conclusion** is a decision or judgment you make that is based on facts and information. **Syllogisms** help organize information so that readers can draw a conclusion based on facts. In a syllogism, all the information you need to draw a conclusion is given in two statements called **premises**. Read the two syllogisms below. Note the underlined words and the letters above them. Think about the premises in each syllogism. The first syllogism is correct; the second is incorrect.

	Syllogism 1	Syllogism 2
	A B	A B
First premise:	All horses eat hay.	All horses eat hay.
	C A	C B
Second premise:	Jingle is a horse.	A deer eats hay.
	C B	C A
Conclusion:	Jingle eats hay.	A deer is a horse.

The pattern AB, CA, CB and thinking about the premises will help you recognize a correct syllogism.

Now read each of the following syllogisms. On your paper, write *correct* if the syllogism is correct and *incorrect* if it is incorrect.

1. First premise: All tarantulas are spiders.
    Second premise: All spiders have eight legs.
    Conclusion: Tarantulas have eight legs.

2. First premise: All languages have meaning.
    Second premise: The Russian language has meaning.
    Conclusion: All languages are Russian.

3. First premise: All snakes shed their skin.
    Second premise: A boa constrictor is a snake.
    Conclusion: A boa constrictor sheds its skin.

B. Expanding Your Skill

Discuss each syllogism with your classmates. If the syllogism is correct, explain how the premises lead to the conclusion. If the syllogism is incorrect, explain the error that was made. On your paper, rewrite any incorrect syllogism to make it correct.

C. Exploring Language

Read each of the following syllogisms. For each pair of premises, write a conclusion on your paper.

1. First premise: All cats have whiskers.
    Second premise: A lion is a kind of cat.
    Conclusion: _____

2. First premise: All citrus fruits contain vitamin C.
    Second premise: An orange is a citrus fruit.
    Conclusion: _____

3. First premise: Only a native-born American can become president of the United States.
    Second premise: Ronald Reagan was president of the United States from 1981 to 1989.
    Conclusion: _____

4. First premise: All reference books give factual information.
    Second premise: An encyclopedia is a reference book.
    Conclusion: _____

5. First premise: Only living things can breathe.
    Second premise: A rock is not a living thing.
    Conclusion: _____

D. Expressing Yourself

Choose one of these activities.

1. Use Part C as a guide, work in two teams to create syllogisms; omit the conclusion that can be drawn. Teams take turns reading their premises to the other team. A correct conclusion scores one point for the guessing team. An incorrect syllogism scores a point for the asking team.

2. On an index card, write a conclusion of some sort. Exchange conclusions with a classmate, and write two premises that lead to your classmate's conclusion. Share premises and conclusions with the rest of the class.

3. Think of a syllogism. Then get three index cards. On one card write the first premise; on the second card, the second premise; and on the third card, the conclusion. Mix up the cards. Ask your classmates to put the cards in order.